Relax with
Baroque Piano

35 Beautiful Pieces

Selected by
Samantha Ward

ED 13849
ISMN 979-0-2201-3681-8
ISBN 978-1-84761-397-4

www.schott-music.com

Mainz · London · Berlin · Madrid · New York · Paris · Prague · Tokyo · Toronto
© 2016 SCHOTT MUSIC Ltd, London · Printed in Germany

ED 13849
British Library Cataloguing-in-Publication Data.
A catalogue record for this book is available from the British Library
ISMN 979-0-2201-3681-8
ISBN 978-1-84761-397-4
© 2016 Schott Music Ltd, London

Cover design by www.josellopis.com
French translation: Michaëla Rubi
German translation: Heike Brühl
Printed in Germany · S&Co.9284

Contents

Introduction

Schott Music's *Relax With* series is designed to help you unwind with some of the piano repertoire's greatest works, alongside lesser known pieces from the Baroque period right through to the 20th century. I have tried to include as many different styles and techniques as possible, whilst remaining within the boundaries of 'relaxing' pieces of music. It has been particularly enjoyable for me to delve into new works in producing these five collections, and to be able to include pieces by the most famous composers as well as by those who are less well known, such as Johanna Senfter, Xaver Scharwenka and, in the Folk collection, works from around the world by Georges Ivanovitch Gurdjieff and Thomas de Hartmann. I hope you enjoy the collections and that you too get to know new pieces along the way.
In this book, I have included pieces written specifically for the piano as well as some orchestral pieces which have been transcribed for you to enjoy, such as a selection of *The Four Seasons* by Vivaldi.

Samantha Ward

Samantha Ward is a British Concert pianist, and founder and Artistic Director of the international festival and summer school, *Piano Week*. For more information, please visit **www.samanthaward.org**

Introduction

La collection « Moments détente » des éditions Schott est conçue pour vous aider à vous relaxer grâce à quelques-unes des plus grandes œuvres du répertoire pour piano ainsi que d'autres moins connues, de la période baroque à nos jours. Je me suis attaché à inclure dans cette sélection des techniques et des styles aussi variés que possible sans perdre de vue les propriétés « relaxantes » de la musique. J'ai eu beaucoup de plaisir à rechercher de nouveaux morceaux dans la perspective des cinq recueils de cette collection et me suis réjoui d'avoir la possibilité de choisir aussi bien des œuvres des compositeurs les plus célèbres que celles d'autres bien moins connus tels que Johanna Senfter ou Xaver Scharwenka ou, parmi les musiques du monde, celles de Georges Ivanovitch Gurdjieff et Thomas de Hartmann. J'espère que vous apprécierez ces recueils et qu'ils vous permettront à vous aussi de découvrir de nouvelles œuvres.
Pour ce volume, j'ai sélectionné des pièces écrites spécifiquement pour le piano ainsi que quelques œuvres orchestrales transcrites pour vous, notamment des extraits des *Quatre Saisons* de Vivaldi.

Samantha Ward

Fondatrice et directrice artistique du festival international et des cours d'été « Piano Week », Samantha Ward est une pianiste concertiste britannique. Vous trouverez davantage d'informations sur son site **www.samanthaward.org**

Einleitung

Mit der Reihe *Relax With* von Schott Music kann man mit vielen bekannten Klavierwerke sowie einigen weniger bekannten Stücken vom Barock bis zum 20. Jahrhundert entspannen. Ich habe versucht, so viele verschiedene Stilrichtungen und Techniken wie möglich zu berücksichtigen und dabei trotzdem den Aspekt der Entspannung nicht aus den Augen zu verlieren. Bei der Zusammenstellung der fünf Sammlungen war es für mich besonders schön, neue Werke kennen zu lernen und Stücke der ganz großen, aber auch Stücke von weniger bekannten Komponisten wie z. B. Johanna Senfter, Xaver Scharwenka und – in der Volksmusik-Sammlung – Werke aus aller Welt von Georges Ivanovitch Gurdjieff und Thomas de Hartmann in die Bände aufzunehmen. Ich wünsche Ihnen viel Spaß mit den Sammlungen und hoffe, dass auch Sie darin einige neue Stücke finden.
Dieses Buch enthält Stücke, die für Klavier geschrieben wurden, aber auch einige Orchesterstücke, die für Klavier bearbeitet wurden, z. B. eine Auswahl aus Vivaldis *Vier Jahreszeiten*.

Samantha Ward

Samantha Ward ist eine britische Konzertpianistin sowie die Gründerin und künstlerische Leiterin von *Piano Week*, einem internationalen Festival und Ferienkurs. Weitere Informationen finden Sie im Internet unter **www.samanthaward.org**

Menuet
G major

Johann Sebastian Bach
(1685–1750)

From the Schott edition *Easy Baroque Piano Music* (ED 5096)

Menuet

G minor

Johann Sebastian Bach
(1685–1750)

From the Schott edition *Easy Baroque Piano Music* (ED 5096)

Trumpet Tune

Henry Purcell
(1659–1695)

From the Schott edition *Easy Baroque Piano Music* (ED 5096)

Sarabande
from BWV 821

Johann Sebastian Bach
(1685–1750)

From the Schott edition *Bach: Selected Works* (ED 5180)

Solfeggio
D major

Johann Christoph Friedrich Bach
(1732–1795)

From the Schott edition *Pianissimo: Für Elise* (ED 20044)

Praeludium
from BWV 846

Johann Sebastian Bach
(1685–1750)

Moderato, tranquillo e legato

From the Schott edition *Bach: Selected Works* (ED 5180)

Menuet
G major
from the *Notebook of Anna Magdalena Bach*

Johann Sebastian Bach
(1685–1750)

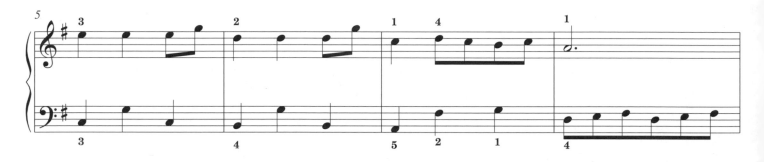

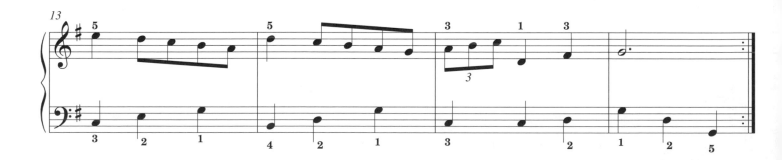

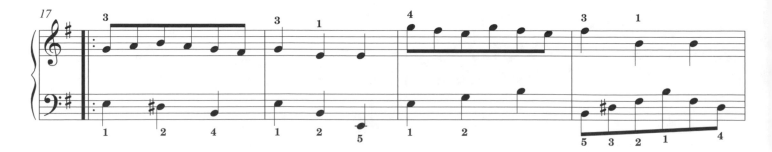

From the Schott edition *Easy Baroque Piano Music* (ED 5096)

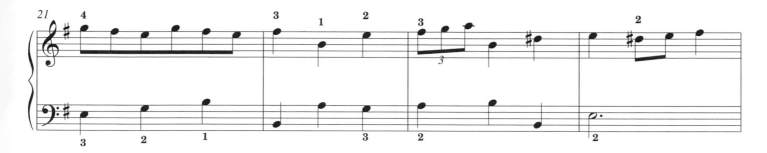

Praeludium
C minor
from *12 Little Preludes*
BWV 999

Johann Sebastian Bach
(1685–1750)

From the Schott edition *Pianissimo: Für Elise* (ED 20044)

Gavotte

Henry Purcell
(1659–1695)

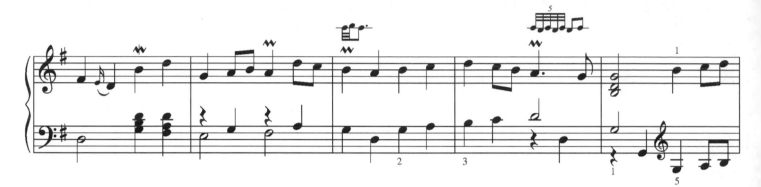

From the Schott edition *Easy Baroque Piano Music* (ED 5096)

Prélude
from *Te Deum*

Marc-Antoine Charpentier
(1643–1704)
Arr. Hans-Günther Heumann

From the Schott edition *Pianissimo: Eine kleine Nachtmusik* (ED 20764)

Ombra mai fù

from the Opera *Xerxes*

HWV 40

George Frideric Handel
(1685–1759)
Arr. Hans-Günther Heumann

From the Schott edition *Pianissimo: Eine kleine Nachtmusik* (ED 20764)

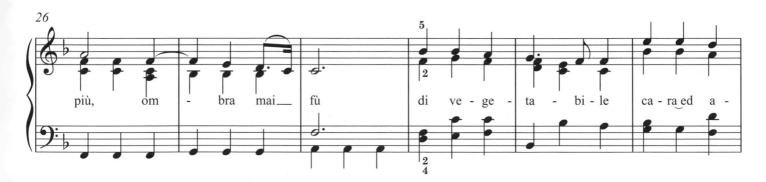

Translation of Italian Lyrics: *Never was the shade / of any plant / dearer and more lovely / or more sweeter*

Sonata

E minor

K291

Domenico Scarlatti
(1685–1757)

From the Schott edition *Scarlatti: Famous Piano Pieces* (ED 9038)

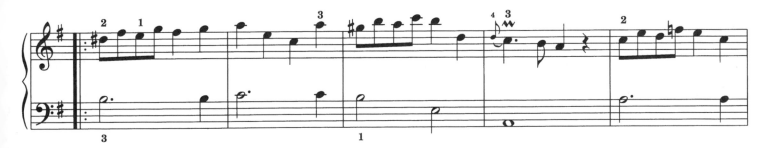

Autumn
3rd movement from *The Four Seasons*
Op. 8/3

Antonio Vivaldi
(1678–1741)
Arr. Hans-Günther Heumann

Allegro ♪ = 138

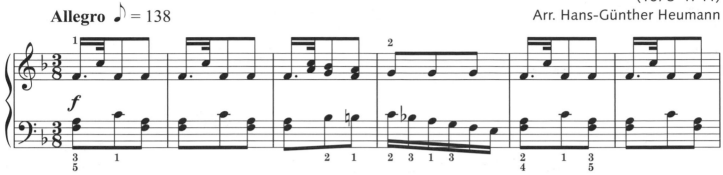

From the Schott edition *Pianissimo: Eine kleine Nachtmusik* (ED 20764)

Air

Henry Purcell
(1659–1695)

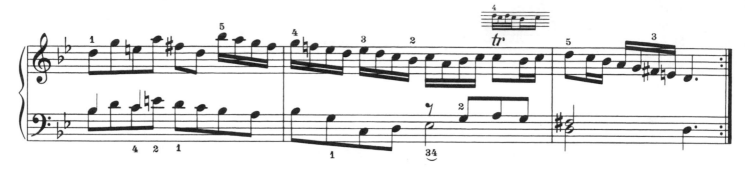

From the Schott edition *Easy Baroque Piano Music* (ED 5096)

This page is left blank to save an unnecessary page turn.

Praeludium

Johann Kuhnau
(1660–1722)

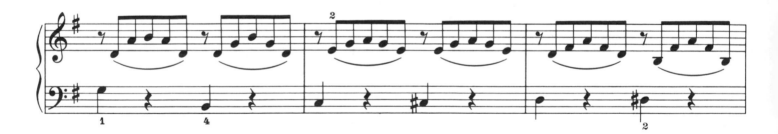

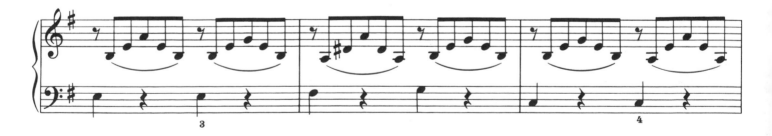

From the Schott edition *Easy Baroque Piano Music* (ED 5096)

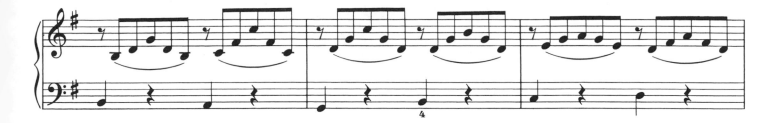

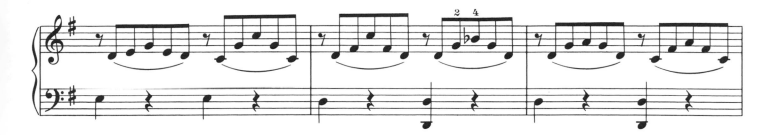

Lascia ch'io pianga

from the Opera *Rinaldo*

George Frideric Handel
(1685–1759)
Arr. Hans-Günther Heumann

From the Schott edition *Pianissimo: Eine kleine Nachtmusik* (ED 20764)

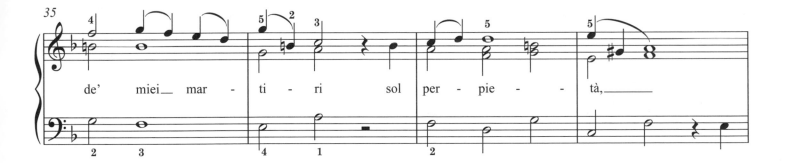

Fine

Il   duo - lo in - fran - ga   que - ste   ri - tor - te,

de'   miei   mar - ti - ri   sol   per - pie - tà,

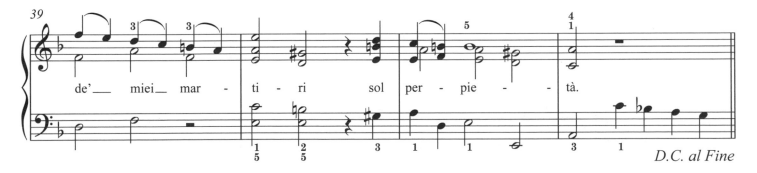

de'___ miei___ mar - ti - ri   sol   per - pie - tà.

D.C. al Fine

Translation of Italian Lyrics: *Allow that I weep over / my cruel fate, / and that I may sigh / for the freedom. /*
Let my sadness shatter / these chains / of my suffering / if only out of pity.

Winter
2nd movement from *The Four Seasons*
Op. 8/4

Antonio Vivaldi
(1678–1741)
Arr. Hans-Günther Heumann

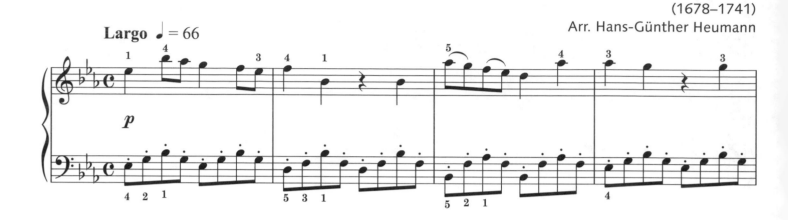

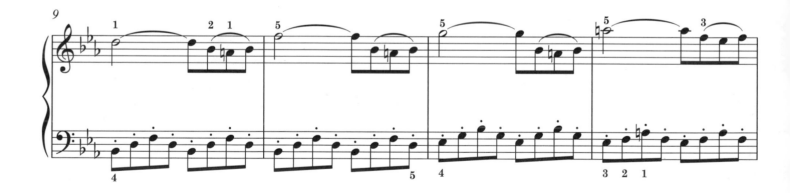

From the Schott edition *Pianissimo: Eine kleine Nachtmusik* (ED 20764)

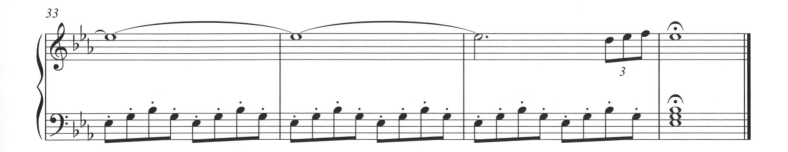

Larghetto

Johann Christoph Friedrich Bach
(1732–1795)

From the Schott edition *Klaviermusik der Klassik* (ED 4747)

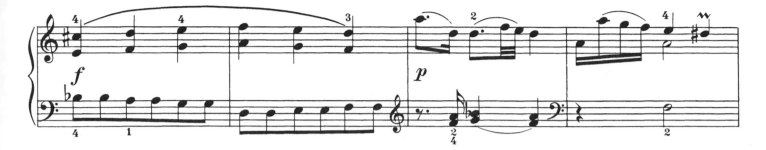

Sonata
F major
K274

Domenico Scarlatti
(1685–1757)

Andante

From the Schott edition *Scarlatti: Famous Piano Pieces* (ED 9038)

Canon
D major

Johann Pachelbel
(1653–1706)
Arr.: Hans-Günter Heumann

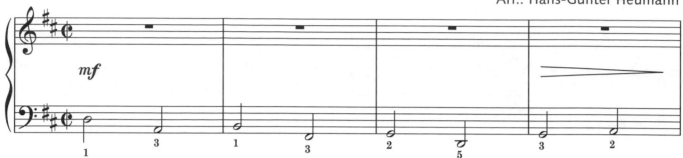

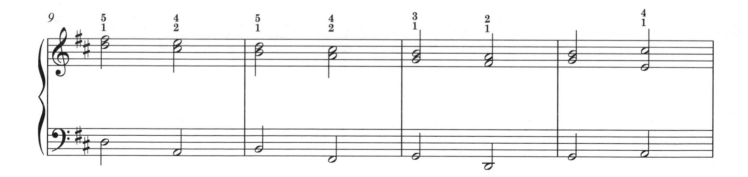

From the Schott edition *The Classical Piano Method: Repertoire Collection 3* (ED 13573)

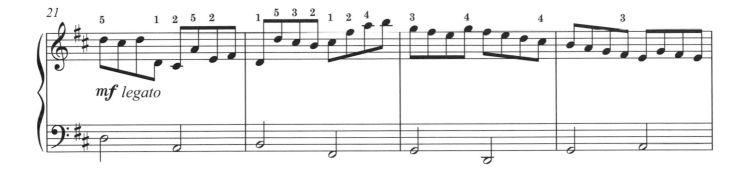

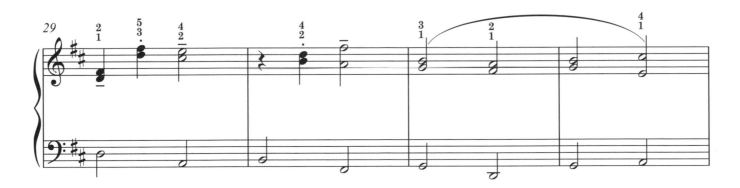

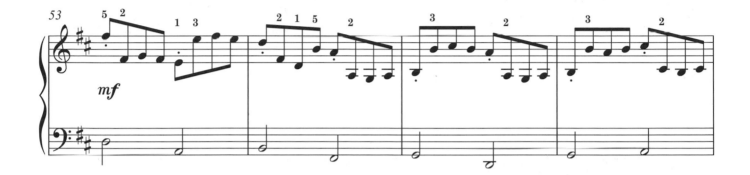

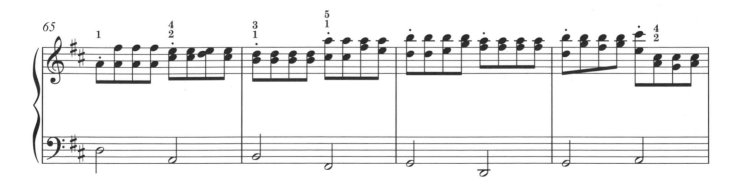

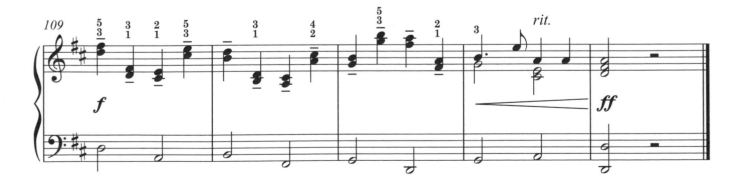

Air

from *Water Music*, Suite No. 1

HWV 348

George Frideric Handel
(1685–1759)
Arr. Hans-Günther Heumann

From the Schott edition *Pianissimo: Eine kleine Nachtmusik* (ED 20764)

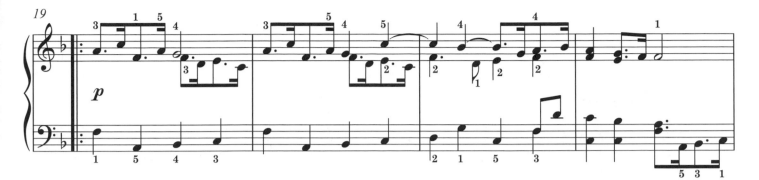

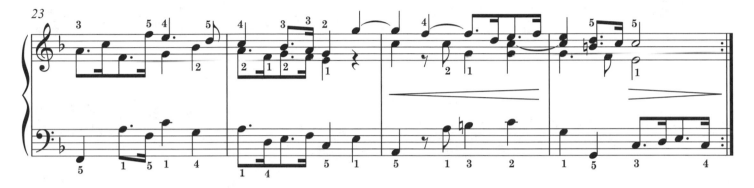

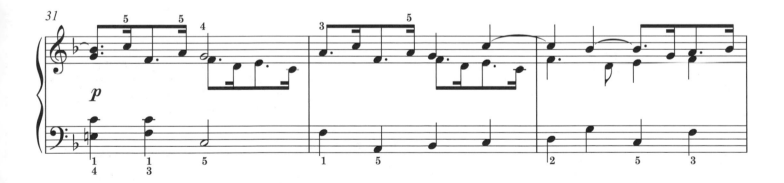

Trio

George Frideric Handel
(1685–1759)

From the Schott edition *Handel: Selected Works* (ED 506)

This page is left blank to save an unnecessary page turn.

Sinfonia

from Cantata No. 156

Johann Sebastian Bach
(1685–1750)
Arr. Hans-Günther Heumann

From the Schott edition *Pianissimo: Eine kleine Nachtmusik* (ED 20764)

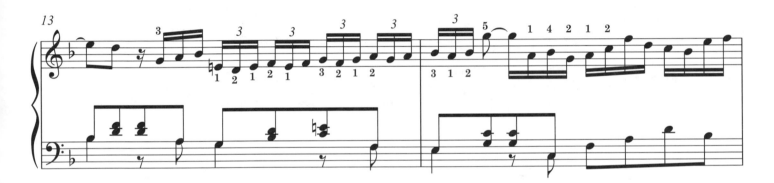

Sonata

D minor

K9

Domenico Scarlatti
(1685–1757)

Allegro

From the Schott edition *Scarlatti: Famous Piano Pieces* (ED 9038)

Spring
1st movement from *The Four Seasons*
Op. 8/1

Antonio Vivaldi
(1678–1741)
Arr. Hans-Günther Heumann

Allegro ♩ = 96

From the Schott edition *Pianissimo: Eine kleine Nachtmusik* (ED 20764)

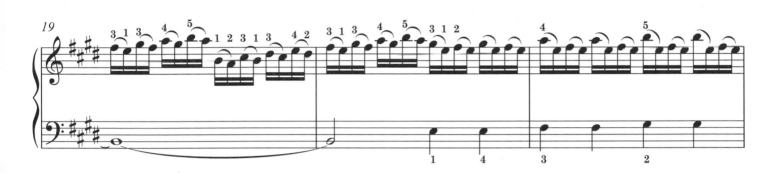

Sarabande
from Suite in D minor, HWV 437

George Frideric Handel
(1685–1759)

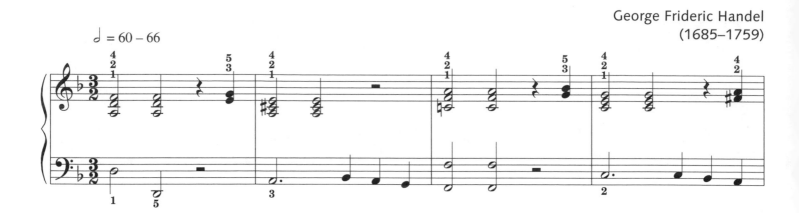

From the Schott edition *Pianissimo: Für Elise* (ED 20044)

Variation 1

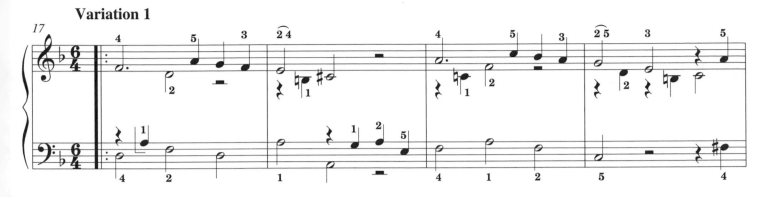

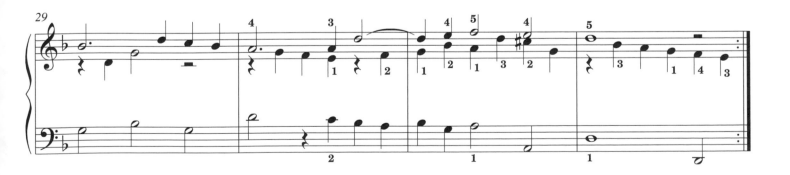

Variation 2

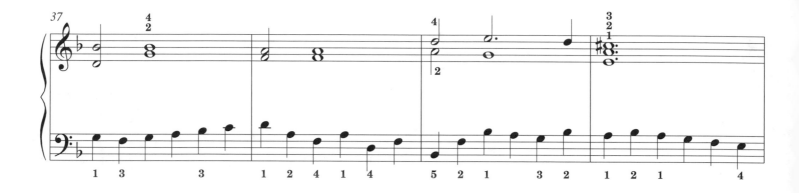

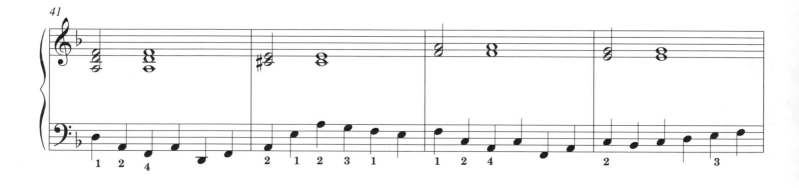

This page is left blank to save an unnecessary page turn.

Sonata

E major

K380

Domenico Scarlatti
(1685–1757)

Andante commodo

From the Schott edition *Scarlatti: Famous Piano Pieces* (ED 9038)

Jesu, Joy of Man's Desiring
from Cantata No. 147

Johann Sebastian Bach
(1685–1750)
Arr. Hans-Günther Heumann

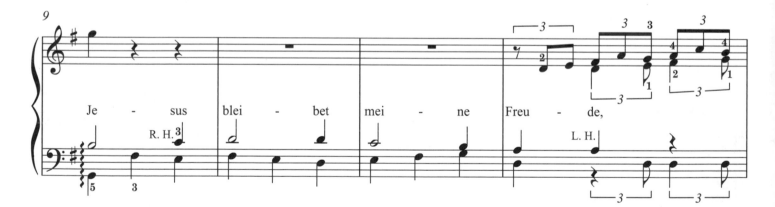

From the Schott edition *Pianissimo: Eine kleine Nachtmusik* (ED 20764)

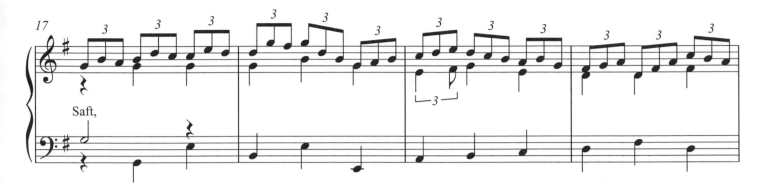

aus   dem   Her -   zen   und   Ge -   sicht.

Translation of German Lyrics: *Jesus remains my joy, / my heart's comfort and essence, / Jesus resists all suffering, / He is my life's strength, / my eye's desire and sun, / my soul's love and joy; / so will I not leave Jesus / out of heart and face*

Aria
from *Goldberg Variations*
BWV 988

Johann Sebastian Bach
(1685–1750)

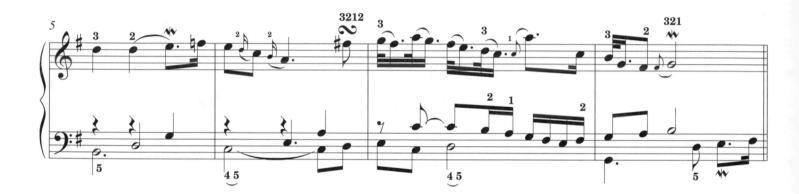

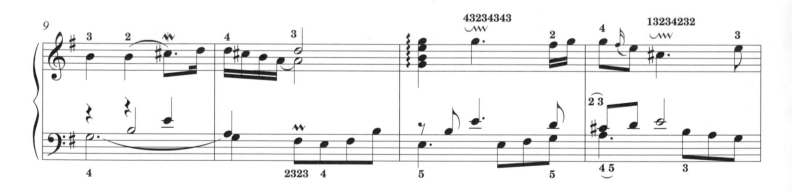

From the Schott edition *Pianissimo: Liebestraum* (ED 20573)

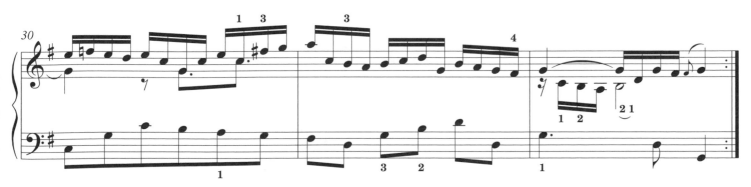

Sleepers Wake

from Cantata No. 140

Johann Sebastian Bach
(1685–1750)
Arr. Helmut Alsdorf

From the Schott edition *Pianissimo: Eine kleine Nachtmusik* (ED 20764)

Air

from Orchestral Suite No. 3 in D major
BWV 1068

Johann Sebastian Bach
(1685–1750)
Arr. Hans-Günther Heumann

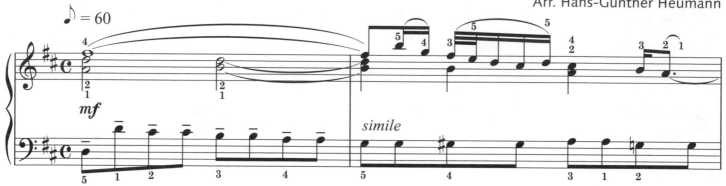

From the Schott edition *Pianissimo: Eine kleine Nachtmusik* (ED 20764)

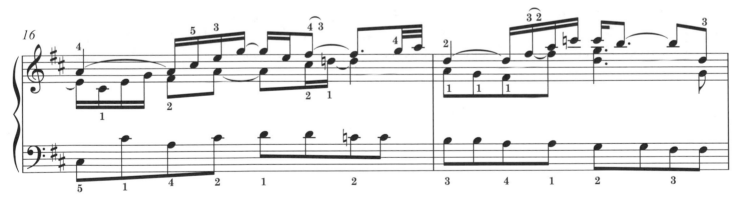

Chaconne
from Suite in D minor
HWV 447

George Frideric Handel
(1685–1759)

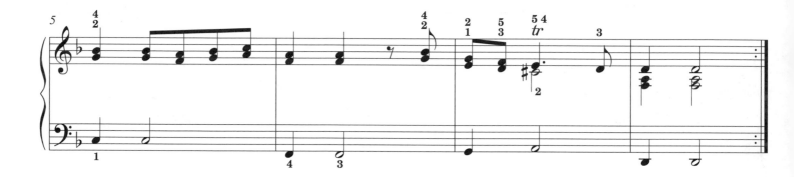

Variation I

ossia: nur beim 1. Mal

From the Schott edition *Pianissimo: Für Elise* (ED 20044)

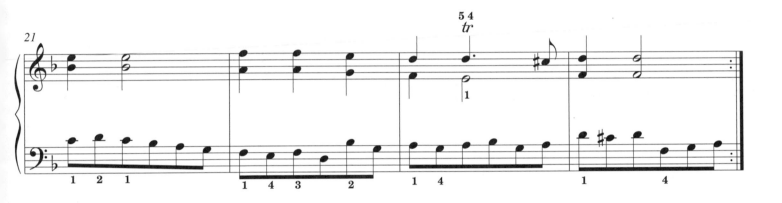

Variation III

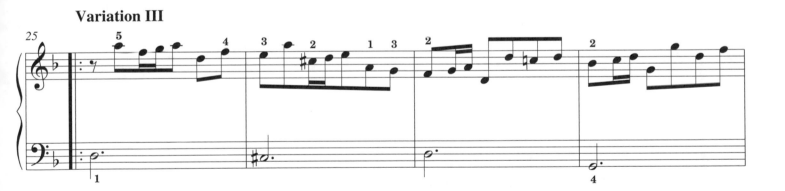

Variation IV

Variation V

Variation VI

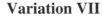

Variation VII

Variation VIII

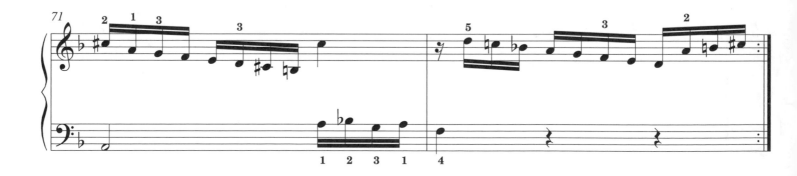

Variation IX

Variation X

Rigaudon
from the Opera *Dardanus*

Jean Philippe Rameau
(1683–1764)

From the Schott edition *Rigaudon* (ED0 910)

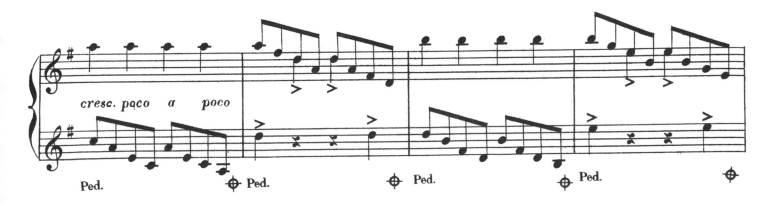

TRIO

Allegretto

The Harmonious Blacksmith

from Suite in E major

HWV 430

George Frideric Handel
(1685–1759)

Air

Variation 1

From the Schott edition *Pianissimo: Liebestraum* (ED 20573)

Variation 2

88

Variation 3

Variation 4

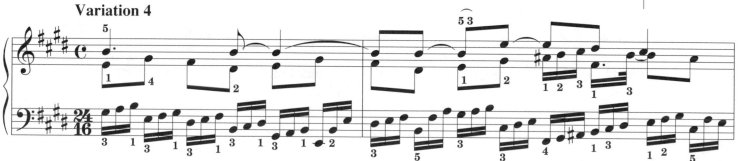

Variation 5

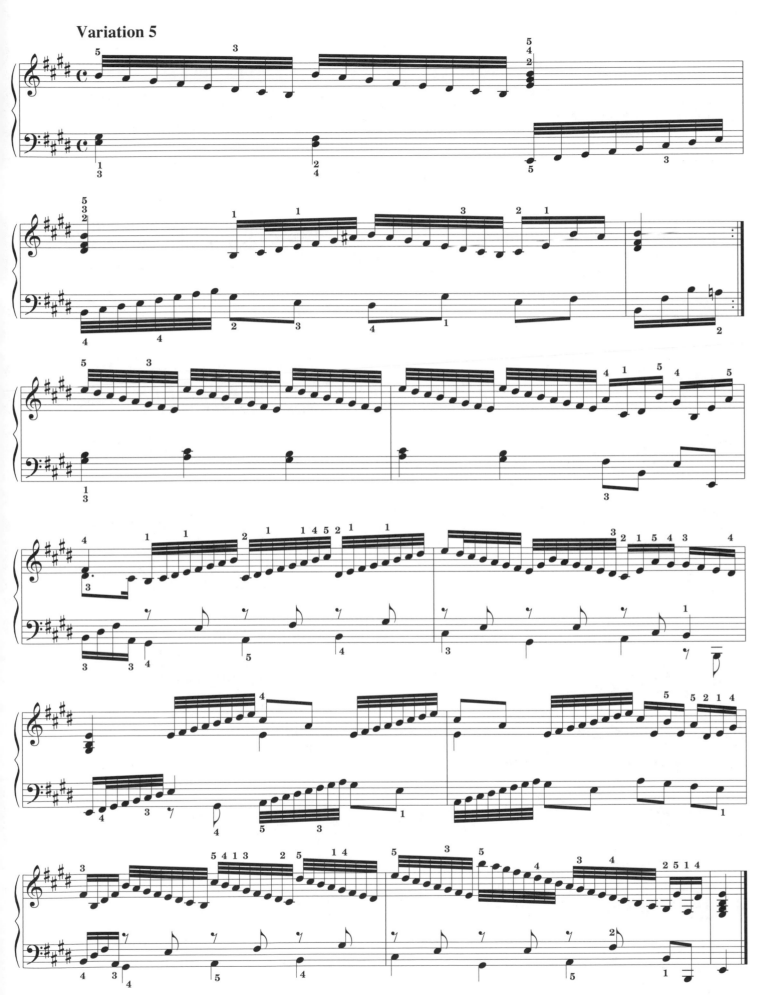

Le Coucou

Rondeau

Claude Daquin
(1694–1772)

L.H. eine Oktave tiefer – *la m.g. a l'octave inférieure*
left hand an octave lower

Drei verschiedene Fingersätze   *3 doigtés différents*   3 different fingerings

usw. wie vorher
ainsi de suite comme auparavant
etc. as before

From the Schott edition *Le Coucou* (ED0 899)

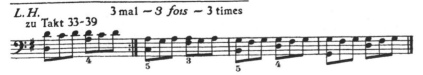

L.H.
zu Takt 33-39   3 mal — 3 fois — 3 times

D. C. al Fine

Schott Music Ltd, London S&Co.9284